33 Moral Stories

Compiled by

'KUNWAR' ANIL KUMAR

MANOJ PUBLICATIONS

CONTENTS

Manoj Publications

761, Main Road Burari, Delhi-110084
Phone : 27611116, 27611349
Fax : 27611546, Mobile : 9868112194
E-mail : manojpublications@vsnl.net
Website : www.manojpublications.com
ISBN : 81-8133-418-3

Showroom :

1583-84, Dariba Kalan,
Chandani Chowk, Delhi-6
Phone : 23262174, 23268216
Mobile : 9818753569

Printers :
Jain Offset Printers

THE POPPY'S RIDDLE

A witch transformed a beautiful girl into a poppy in a field. Each evening she was allowed to return to her normal self and go home to spend the night with her parents.

One morning, before she went back to the field to be transformed into a poppy again, she said to her mother, "If you succeed in picking me, the witch's magic spell will be broken."

That was true, but how could the girl's mother recognize her amongst all the other thousands of poppies. The answer was simple. Since the girl had spent the night at home, she was the only poppy in the field which was not wet with dew.

THE BATTLE BETWEEN WEASELS AND MICE

WHEN the weasels and the mice went at war, it were the mice who were defeated. The mice held a meeting and after much deliberation came to the conclusion that it was their unorganised way of fighting that they had to face the defeat. So the mice appointed some commanders. The commanders, then, to set themselves apart from the ordinary soldiers made themselves helmets fitted with long horns.

When the next battle was fought it was again won by the weasels. The mice, somehow, saved themselves by retreating into their holes. But the commanders could not get in because of those long horns on their helmets and were devoured by the weasels.

A TINY GRASSHOPPER'S ADVICE TO A DONKEY

A donkey was not happy with his hoarse voice. One day, while he was grazing in a field, he met a grasshopper who was singing a delightful song. The donkey was so captivated with the grasshopper's music that he asked the grasshopper, "Tell me the secret of your sweet voice."

"It's dew," replied the grasshopper jocularly, "that I eat every morning."

So the donkey started eating grass with great enthusiasm especially at the break of the dawn, when the grass was covered with dew. His voice never changed, but fortunately he became fatter and fatter day by day.

□□

ELECTRA AND HER SUITORS

IN the constellation of Taurus, Aldebaran the most luminous star, fell in love with Electra, the most enchanting star of the Pleiades. Aldebarán was unaware of Alcyon, a rival suitor of Electra and came to know about him only when he attacked his herd of camels on the way.

These two aspirants are still fighting with each other and even now, on calm nights, one can see pale blue Electra followed by red Alcyon and then by Aldebaran with his herd of heavenly camels making up the constellation of the Hyades.

THE REWARD OF THE WOLF

WHEN a fishbone got stuck in the throat of a wolf, he went to a heron and asked for his help. "I shall reward you handsomely, if you could please help me."

The heron agreed and the next moment he thrust his long neck down the throat of the wolf and pulled out the fishbone. The wolf thanked the heron and began to leave.

The heron shouted after him, "What about my reward you promised a moment ago?"

"What reward?" said the wolf. "Is it not sufficient that I was kind enough not to bite off your head when you inserted it in my mouth? I have spared your life. You should consider yourself lucky to get a reward of your life."

THE FLIGHT OF A STAG

THE stag's magestic set of antlers was the cause of his immense pride. But, however, he was not the least happy with his slender legs and hoofs.

One day, a lion began to chase him. The stag darted away in a flash and succeeded in fleeing from the lion, but unfortunately he ran into a thicket. His antlers were caught in the overhanging branches and he could flee no more. The stag, before he was killed by the lion, thought to himself, "How wrong I was to curse my slender legs, which carried me to safety. How wrong I was to take pride in my large antlers, which have now become the cause of my doom."

A HARE'S SATISFACTION

A hare was cursing himself for being so cowardly all the time and for running away at the slightest click. Just as he was preparing himself to face the life with courage, a sudden noise again made him jump at his feet and run away as fast as he could.

He came to a pool, where, as soon as, the frogs saw him coming, dived into the water and hid themselves.

"Thank goodness!" thought the hare to himself. "I am not the only one who is a coward, there are others too who are even more cowardly."

WE SHOULD NOT CRITICIZE NATURE

Two boys were playing in a garden. They saw blackberries in a tree. Their mouth began watering. They wanted to eat them. But the tree was too high. The problem was how to get the blackberries.

One of the boys said, "Sometimes nature makes grave mistakes. It has grown little fruits like blackberries on a very high tree, whereas a heavy fruit like watermelon grows on the ground."

The other one nodded in agreement and said, "I quite agree with

what you say. It sounds quite logical. But I fail to understand why nature doesn't understand the logics of proportion. Now you see how silly is it that one has to climb so high and take all the pains of climbing for such small fruits. I personally feel that nature is not perfect."

All of a sudden, a bunch of blackberries fell on the head of a boy. He looked up but didn't say anything.

But the other boy said, "Friends, we were criticizing the nature a moment ago and the nature has given us a lesson. Just imagine if it had been watermelon instead of blackberries, it would have broken your head and you would have been no more."

"Oh yes, nature is perfect and is beyond criticism," said the boy.

❏❏

THE POTTER'S TRUTH

LONG, long ago, in a village there lived a potter by the name of Yudhistrira. He was in a habit of drinking liquor, One day, he stumbled on a borken pot in a drunken state and fell down. The sharp edge of the broken pot pierced his forehead and he started bleeding profusely. He didn't care much for his wound. The wound got worse. Even after it had healed, it had left a big scar on his forehead.

After sometime, there was a famine in the country. The potter lost his business. He, then, left for some other part of the country. There he, somehow, got himself employed in the king's service.

Once, the king noticed the big scar on the forehead of the potter, he thought to himself that the potter must be a brave man. The scar was most probably the result of his face to face fight with some soldier of the enemy.

So, the king decided to place the potter amongst his chosen army generals. As the war was impending, the king decided to bestow honour on generals to encourage them.

Later the king decided to make the potter the chief of the army. So he asked the potter, "General, what's your name? How did you get this scar on your forehead? What was the name of the battle you fought in?"

"Your Majesty," replied the potter, "I'm a potter by profession. Once I fell down on a broken pot in a drunken state and got wounded. This scar is the result of the wound."

Hearing this, the king was very much dejected. He ordered his soldiers to throw the potter out of the army.

The potter begged for king's forgiveness. He requested the king to keep him in royal service, so that he could prove his worth in the army, but the king refused and sternly ordered his expulsion from the army and the kingdom.

Moral—*If you speak the truth, sometimes it may go against you.*

THE TRAP OF THE FOX

WHEN it was time to elect their new king, the animals elected the monkey to this all powerful position, because of his antics. The fox was very much disappointed and waited for a chance.

One day, the fox found a delicious fruit lying in the way. He was quick to understand that it was a trap. He offered it to the monkey king and told him about the place where it was lying.

The greedy monkey king hastily reached the spot with the hope of getting more fruits. Instead, he was trapped. The fox laughed and said, "Your antics and not your intellect may amuse the animals. Better sit in the trees only and not on the throne."

□□

THE WISE CAT AND THE WISER MOUSE

I⊤ was a warehouse where the mice lived. One day, a black cat wandered into it.

"What a good place for me to live in and feed on mice. I will pretend to be dead," thought the cat to himself and lay down on the ground. The younger mice surrounded him and began to shout, "Look, here is a dead cat."

But, an old mouse cautioned them—"Be careful, a cat has nine lives." Then the old mouse climbed up a large bin where a sack of flour was kept. It was just above where the cat lay. The mouse cut open the sack and the flour poured out onto the cat. Then there came a sneeze and a white cat came out of the flour.

□□

THE ATHLETE WHO JUMPED TOO HIGH

He was, of course, an athlete, but very ambitious and loud-mouthed. One day, tired of being jeered at by the spectators at home, he decided to leave his country and put up his show abroad.

When he returned home he began to tell his stories of success to each and everyone. He would say: "In Sydney, I jumped so high, I was out of sight. It took many days for me to return to the ground. If you are not convinced, go and ask anyone there."

"Why should I?" said the listener. "Why don't you jump out of sight right now, forever?"

THE LION AND HIS BUSINESS PARTNERS

WHEN the jackal, the wolf and the hyena went into business with the lion, it was agreed that losses and profits will be shared equally by all the four. It so happened that, one day, they hunted a buffalo and then a shareholders meeting was held to divide the game into four equal parts. The meeting was chaired by the lion who

pronounced thus: "I will take the first share, because I am the king of the forest. The second and the third shares also belong to me, because it is I who hunted it. Now if anyone of you lays claims on the fourth share, he may do so at his own risk because I am already feeling hungry.' Thank you, gentlemen! That's all."

☐☐

A FATHER'S DILEMMA

H<small>E</small> was a proud father of two beautiful daughters. While the younger one was married to a poor farmer the elder was married to a potter. Once the father decided to invite his daughters. First, he invited his younger daughter and asked her, "How is the business going on?"

"Fine!" replied the daughter. "But our land needs more irrigation. Pray to God for heavy rains."

Then he put up the same question to his elder daughter. She said, "It's all going on well. But pray for dry weather to harden our pots."

And imagine the dilemma of the poor father. "What should I pray for!" he exclaimed. "My two daughters have two different wishes."

THE ARAB AND THE BEGGAR

An Arab, while passing through the market place, was stopped by a beggar. The beggar asked the rich Arab for some clothes in the name of Allah. Since the clothing was begged in the name of Allah, the Arab could not refuse it. But he decided to give his oldest suit to the beggar. Putting it on, the beggar according to custom, hung a sign on the collar which said, "There is no god but Allah."

"But you have not added" said the Arab, "'and Mohammed is His Prophet' as the second traditional sentence."

"I will not," said the beggar. "Because this suit was stitched much before the Prophet's arrival in this world."

MIDAS TOUCH

THERE was a king named Midas. He had enormous riches. His kingdom was very large and wide. But he was not satisfied with his wealth and kingdom. He wanted to be more wealthy and extend his kingdom to farther limits.

King Midas had a lovely young daughter. He loved her very much. She was the apple of his eyes. He wanted to marry her to a prince worthy of her in all respects. But before his daughter's marriage, he wanted to have more riches.

In order to have more, king Midas started praying God. He continuously prayed for many days without taking food and water. God was pleased with his prayer. He appeared before Midas and said to him, "You have got everything in the world. What is it that you want to get from me now? I am pleased with you so I shall fulfil your desire."

Midas said, "I wish to have lots and lots of wealth. Please bless me that whatever I touch, shall become gold."

God said, "Have you pondered over your wish?"

Midas said happily, "Oh yes, My Lord, I have given a serious thought to my wish. In fact, I have thought about it for a long time. Please fulfil it."

God said, "All right! I grant you your wish." Saying so God disappeared.

Midas was overjoyed. He began moving around in the palace and touching everything happily. Everything he touched became gold. He was deriving utmost satisfaction from the situation. Suddenly he realised that he hadn't eaten anything for days together and was feeling terribly hungry. He clapped. The servants came running. King Midas asked them to bring food for him.

As soon as he touched the food to eat, it turned into gold. The king was filled with horror and surprise. Now he realised why God had asked him to ponder over his wish. He was able to understand the gravity of the situation. He was feeling hungry and he could not eat anything. What he took to be a boon, turned out to be a curse for him. King Midas became perplexed. He was so confused that when his daughter came to him, he, very unmindfully, picked her up; and lo! his daughter too turned into gold.

Now this was something more than too much. He began crying in disgust. But nothing could be done; and who was to be blamed? He had asked for the boon himself. He began praying fervently. After a long wait God appeared before him and said, "what is it that you want now? I have already fulfilled your wish."

"No God, please forgive me," Midas fell in the feet of God and continued saying, "I do not want any such thing. Please make me free from the curse. O God! My greed for riches had made me blind. And please see the result. Look at my daughter! She has turned into gold. Please revert me to my former state."

God said, "All right," and disappeared. Now Midas was happy with his riches and kingdom; and he was all the more happy to see his daughter playing in his lap.

□□

A DOG'S ADVICE TO THE DONKEY

It was, no doubt, a loud noise that made the dog wake up. He pricked up his ears straight and pointed sharply towards the sound and again went to sleep.

The owner's another pet, the donkey noticed it and said in an amazed tone, "Why don't you bark? I am sure there are thieves."

"It is better, you mind your own business", said the dog. But the donkey, in order to prove his faithfulness, began to bray loudly. This, of course, frightened off the thieves, but also awakened the master, who came running. He was so furious at being woken up that he beat the donkey thoroughly with his stick.

After the master had gone, the dog asked the donkey, "How do you feel for not paying heed to a good friendly advice? When a master is like that, one must think, at best, of oneself only, first and foremost."

THE OLD WOLF AND THE SKINNY DOG

THERE was a wolf, who due to old age and physical infirmity, was finding it difficult to manage his meals. Generally his preys outran him in the chase. One day while wandering with a single thought in his mind— 'What should I do now?'—the poor wolf met a street dog, who looked all skin and bones due to the hunger he had to face, after being beaten and chased away by his master.

"How would you like to be a little more generous and allow me to eat you?" said the wolf to the dog happily.

"Lean and thin as I have become," said the dog, "I would advise you to feed me properly and eat me after I have gained some weight. Right now you wouldn't get anything out of me."

Thinking that the idea was not altogether bad allowing the dog to gain a little fat before he is consumed, the wolf arranged food for the dog and got out of his way for a few days; but by that time, the dog, not only had gained enough fat, he had also become strong enough to give a terrific fight to the wolf.

THE RIDDLE OF THE SPHINX

IN the ancient times, a sphinx guarded the city of Thebes. It was a strange creature. He had the head of a woman, the body of a lion and the wings of a falcon.

The sphinx had a habit of asking a riddle to every passer-by and anyone who could not answer the riddle correctly, was gobbled up by him.

One day, the Sphinx asked the same question to Oedipus, the King of Thebes. "What is it that has four legs in the morning, two at noon and three in the evening?"

"A human being," answered Oedipus. "As a child he crawls on his fours, in his youth he walks on his two legs and in his old age he walks around with the help of a staff."

□□

THANKS FOR WHAT ?

ONCE a fox trying to find a cover while being chased by hunters, entered the house of a woodcutter and hid himself under a bed. He requested the woodcutter, who was standing nearby to help him save his life. The woodcutter agreed.

Soon the hunters arrived there and asked the woodcutter if he had seen any fox near his house.

The woodcutter, although spoke in audibly loud tone that he had not seen any fox around, he signalled towards the fox which was hiding in his house. The hunters could not understand what the woodcutter pointed at and went their way. Then the fox came out of his hiding and was ready to leave when the woodcutter said, "Won't you even say 'thanks' to me?"

"'Thanks' for what?" said the fox. "Should it be for the words that you gave me or for the signals that you made to the hunters?"

□□

WE SHOULD NOT CHEAT OTHERS

RATAN and Mohan were good friends. They had great confidence in each other. Once they decided to enjoy their holidays together. They went out to a hill station for a week.

Both enjoyed their stay at the hill station. After seven days, they planned to return. When they reached the station to board the train, they found a bag lying at the station platform.

Ratan noticed it first and picked it up. He opened it and saw that it contained a lot of cash and jewellery in it.

Ratan tried to hide it in his suitcase. But Mohan suggested, "Ratan, we should not keep it with us. Somebody has missed it. We should ask people at the station. If someone claims and is able to tell the exact details, we shall handover this bag to him."

"No, No, you are a fool. Everybody will come to claim it as his own bag. I have found it, so this is mine," Ratan said.

Mohan said, "What are you talking? In case you do not want to give it to its owner, we should divide it into two equal parts. Both of us have found it. We have shared every moment, every food, every joy here together. Therefore, we should divide the cash and jewellery also into two parts to enjoy together."

"I don't agree with you. I saw it first, and so it is mine." Saying so Ratan kept the bag in his possession.

Meanwhile the train arrived at the platform. Ratan and Mohan boarded it. Once they occupied their seats, they were at ease and began talking to each other. Time was rolling on. When the night fell, they began feeling sleepy.

After sometime the train halted at the next station. Suddenly they saw some policemen entering their compartment. Ratan was frightened to see them. He tried to put his suitcase behind his back.

Ratan whispered in Mohan's ear, "We are in great trouble. The police have come. They would arrest us and put us behind bars. You know, we have not stolen the bag."

Mohan said in a low voice, "Why do you say—'us'—and not—'me'? Please don't try to involve me. I have got nothing to do with the bag. You did not listen to me when I asked you to find out the owner and hand over the bag to him. Far from handing it over to the real owner, you even refused to share it with me. And now when you feel that you are going to land in an unpleasant situation, you want to share the unpleasantness with me. Very clever!"

The police saw lines of terror in Ratan's face and became suspicious about him. They searched his belongings and found the bag. This was the bag they had come searching for. They arrested him and sent him to jail.

Now Ratan was repenting that he should have listened to his friend's advice.

❑❑

KING METABO AND HIS JAVELIN

KING Metabo was a famous javelin thrower and also a brave and intelligent fighter.

One day, he along with his little daughter went out hunting. But all of a sudden, he was attacked by his enemies. As he was all alone with only a little girl by his side he had to flee from that place. While fleeing, the king came to a river. It was difficult for him to swim across the river with his daughter on his back. So he tied his daughter with his javelin and hurled it on to the other side of the river.

Then the king himself swam across to where his daughter was. His enemies were disheartened to see the king get out of their hands and were astounded to see his valour.

☐☐

MADONNA AND THE FLOWER

LONG ago, it so happened that a very heavy wagon got stuck in the mud. The wagon driver despite all his efforts could not pull it out. Just then Madonna arrived there by chance. She said to the driver, "If you give me a drink, I will free your wagon."

"Oh sure!" said the driver of the wagon offering her a bottle, "but I do not have a cup."

"I will manage that", said Madonna. She folded a white flower having red stripes, in the shape of a chalice and used it to drink from". Ever since, people call this flower the flower of convolvulus— "The Madonna's Cup."

◻◻

THE SUN, THE MOON AND THE SEA

ONCE upon a time, billions of years ago, the Sun and the Moon lived on the Earth, as husband and wife.

One day, they sent an invitation to the Sea to visit them. The Sea hesitated thinking that his visit might create problems for his host due to his enormous size. But when the Sun and the Moon reassured him, the Sea visited them along with all the marine creatures. But, then the water level began to rise. The Sun and the Moon climbed further up in the sky and since then they have stayed there forever.

ONCE there were two cockerels living in a farmhouse. As each of them wanted to have his hold on the farm house, it was decided to resolve the matter once and for all, by fighting a duel. So both fought tooth and nail and in the end one had to flee the scene.

The winning cockerel was so happy that he flew up onto a high fence and started his cock-a-doodle-doo. This attracted an eagle's attention which swooped down on it and carried it away to his nest on a high mountain. Nature has its own ways of inflicting punishment on those who have an inflated ego.

PEOPLE TAKE ADVANTAGE
OF OTHERS' FIGHT

Two fat cats lived in a village. One cat was black, and the other was brown with dappled skin. They always quarrelled with each other, using their sharp teeth and claws.

One day the black cat while wandering around, saw a piece of bread near a house. She quickly reached there and picked it up.

The brown cat was watching the black cat from a distance. She reached there hurriedly and said to the black cat, "Share this bread with me, or else I shall snatch it from you."

The black cat refused to share it and they began quarrelling. There was a monkey sitting in a tree. He saw them quarrelling and reached there to settle their dispute. But the cats kept on fighting.

The monkey said, "Do not fight my sisters. I am like your elder brother. I shall divide your bread into two equal parts in order to settle your dispute."

Both the cats agreed. The monkey brought a balance. He divided the bread into two parts and put one each on both pans of the balance. Now he lifted the balance to weigh the pieces of the bread.

He saw that one pan of the balance lowered due to the little extra weight on one side. He tore a little from the heavier side to make it weigh equal. He put the excess piece of the bread in his mouth and gobbled it up.

Now weighing the pieces the second time, he found that the other pan of the balance had lowered. He tore another piece from this pan to make it equal. He put the excess piece in his mouth again and gobbled up.

But again the other pan became heavy and lowered. He again tore it. Thus, he tore pieces from both sides of the bread till only small pieces were left. He ate those pieces also and said, "Sisters, since there was hardly anything left on the pans of the weighing balance, I decided to finish that also, and hence I have finished it. I knew the left over quantity would not have been sufficient to assuage your hunger."

The monkey left them staring at each other utterly confused. They had understood that they had been thoroughly cheated by the cunning monkey.

The brown cat with dappled skin said to the black cat, "Sister, what is done cannot be undone; but let us take a lesson from it, and that is—'if we have to avoid being cheated, we have to stop quarrelling'. Let others not take advantage of our feuds."

□□

THE HIGH FLYING CRANE AND THE PEACOCK

It was always the peacock's turn to laugh at the crane. "Yours is a very dull plumage," the peacock would often say to the crane showing him his own. "Look at my golden and purple plumage. You have nothing beautiful, whatsoever, on your body."

"But there is a difference," replied the crane. "While I can fly in the sky and sing to the stars and moon, you simply drag yourself along the ground."

Should it be said, then, that it is far better to be famous in poor clothes rather than die unknown in the midst of wealth?

⬜⬜

33

THE FLAVOUR OF JALEBEES

A car speeded by an old woman. She fell down and lost consciousness. A crowd gathered around her. Some tried to fan air over her and another sprinkled water. A man put a shoe to her nose taking it to be an epileptic fit.

A voice said, "Let's take her to the doctor."

Shiekhchilli was also there working up his brain.

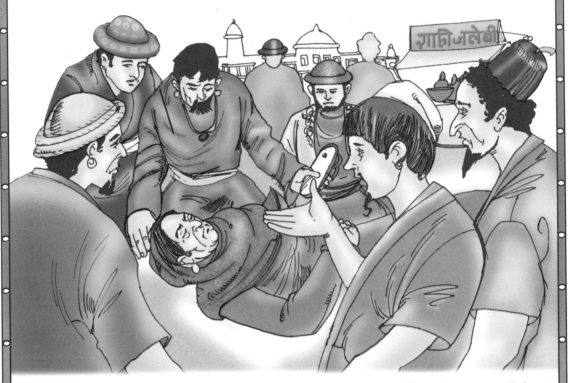

He advised, "I tell you the right thing to do. Get her smell hot Jalebees. Also put some crisp pieces into her mouth."

The people laughed. The old woman opened her eyes and moaned, "Don't laugh. Listen to his wise suggestion."

It was now clear that the old woman was putting on an act of being unconscious. The crowd dispersed. The people felt cheated and cursed the old woman.

The old woman sighed having failed to trick the people.

A FROG'S EFFORT

A frog once decided that he would become as huge as a bull.

So the frog began to inhale more and more air, and the more he breathed, the bigger he became; no doubt.

"Am I huge enough now?" he asked hopefully of his companions, who were watching the show very intently.

His companions then had another look at the bull and said, "No, just a little bit more."

So, the overjoyed frog kept on puffing itself up and up......until its belly burst like a balloon.

It is foolish to make a fool of oneself just for the entertainment of others.

□□

THE LONG AND THE SHORT OF A DINNER

OBEYING the orders of the lion—the forest king, the fox invited the stork over dinner towards the settlement of certain disputes peacefully; even though he did it half heartedly. The fox prepared a tasty soup and served it up on plates. The stork much to his embarrassment was hardly able to have any of it.

Like a true guest, the stork thanked the fox for the tasty dinner, he had served, and left.

Next, it was the turn of the stork to invite the fox over dinner. The stork too cooked a very delicious meal, but he served it in narrow mouthed jars. The fox to his embarrassment found it hard to even insert his nose into the utensils. He had to leave almost hungry.

Playing dirty tricks on others may bring equally dirty responses.

REVENGE OF A NIGHTINGALE

A nightingale lived in a tree. For the last few days she had been making a nest. She was getting ready to lay her eggs in it.

A pair of snakes lived in the burrow of the tree. They were watching the nightingale who was very happy and preparing to lay eggs.

One final day the nightingale laid two eggs. She was chirping happily here and there on the branches of the tree. She did not want to leave her eggs alone.

But she had to go in search of food. So she put dry grass on the eggs to cover them for safety. As soon as she left her nest, the snakes came out, climbed up the tree and ate both the eggs.

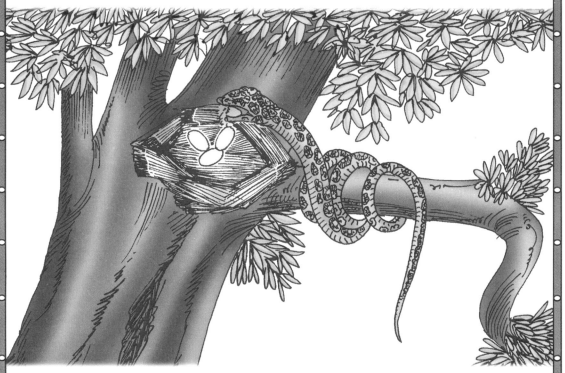

When the nightingale returned, she became very upset to see that her eggs had been eaten away. The egg-shells were lying near the root of the tree. Now she understood everything and decided to exact revenge on the snakes.

The nightingale went to a garden where a king used to come for his morning walks. The nightingale began singing a sweet song. The king was very happy to hear such a nice tune early in the morning.

The nightingale was also aware that the king had become happy to hear her sweet song. The king realised that the sweet song of the nightingale made him feel fresh and he remained happy throughout the day. So the king made it his everyday routine to come to the garden at the right time and hear the warbling of the nightingale.

One day the nightingale did not come to the garden. The king felt sad and asked his guards to find where the nightingale was. The guards could not find the nightingale.

The next day, the nightingale came to the garden, but she was not singing. The king realised that something was wrong with her. He ordered his guards to follow her.

The nightingale flew from there and reached the tree. The guards also reached there following her. They saw that the nightingale was sitting by the side of her nest. There were three eggs in it. She had laid eggs again. The nightingale already had a small pebble in her beak. She deliberately dropped it at the root of the tree. Thinking that an egg had fallen from the nest, the pair of snakes came out of their holes.

The guards saw the snakes. Now they could understand the nightingale's problem. They killed them.

On the next morning, when the king came to the garden, he heard the melodious voice of the nightingale. She was singing in a very happy mood. The king also became very happy.

The nightingale was extremely grateful to the king, as the king had permanently posted guards to take care of her nest. In order to show her gratitude, she would come to the garden every day and make the king happy with her warbling.

□□

THE OLD WOLF AND THE BOLD GOAT

THERE was a wolf who had become old and weak and found it hard to chase his prey and catch it. One day, the wolf was chasing a goat. The goat jumped on to a high rock and saved himself. Then he turned to the wolf and said, "Why should we waste time upon each other? Why not you open your mouth wide and let me jump into it?"

"That is fine", said the wolf and opened his mouth wide. The goat jumped, landing not into the wolf's mouth, but onto his head. It was such a hard landing that the wolf was knocked out. When he regained his consciousness, he could not recall whether he had eaten the goat or not.

THE HUNTER AND THE BEAR

THE hunter was very brave at talking about bears; like some people do when they know that they have to talk and talk only and could do nothing more than that.

Once, while he was searching for a bear in a forest he met a woodcutter and asked him, "My dear brother, do you have the slightest idea, where I can find the footprints of a bear?"

"Plenty of them," said the woodcutter. "Follow me to the bear's den."

"N...No! Thank you, but that won't be necessary," The hunter began to shake with fear. "I am looking only for bear tracks."